The Coffee Lover

by
Linda Kita-Bradley

Grass Roots Press

The Coffee Lover is published by

Grass Roots Press, a division of Literacy Services of Canada Ltd.
Phone: 1-888-303-3213
Website: www.grassrootsbooks.net

ACKNOWLEDGMENTS

We acknowledge the financial support of the Government of Canada through the Canada Book Fund (CBF) for our publishing activities.

Produced with the assistance of the Government of Alberta, Alberta Multimedia Development Fund.

Government of Alberta ■

Editor: Dr. Pat Campbell
Photography: Grass Roots Press
Book design: Lara Minja, Lime Design Inc.

Library and Archives Canada Cataloguing in Publication

Kita-Bradley, Linda, 1958–
    The coffee lover / Linda Kita-Bradley.

ISBN 978–1–926583–76–1

    1. Readers for new literates. 2. Readers—Coffee drinking.
3. Readers—Humor. I. Title.

PE1126.N43K58254 2012   428.6'2   C2011–907580–6

Printed in Canada

This is Bo.

Bo loves coffee.

He makes a pot of coffee.

Bo presses the ON button.

He makes cereal.

Bo makes two bowls of cereal.

Bo eats his cereal.

Bo's son, Dan, eats the cereal.

Bo gets a cup of coffee.

What! No coffee?

Bo checks the coffee maker.

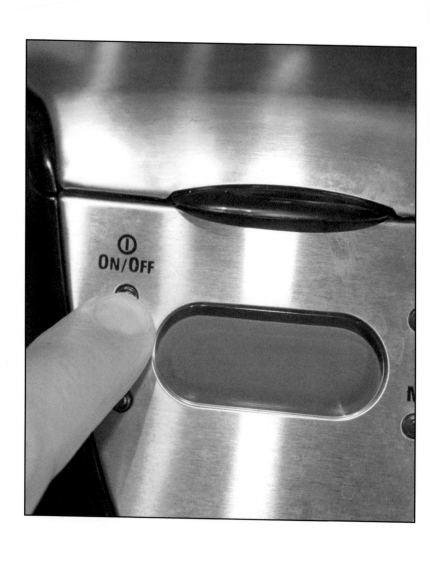

Bo presses the ON button.

He waits for the coffee.

No coffee.

Bo presses the ON button again.

Bo waits.

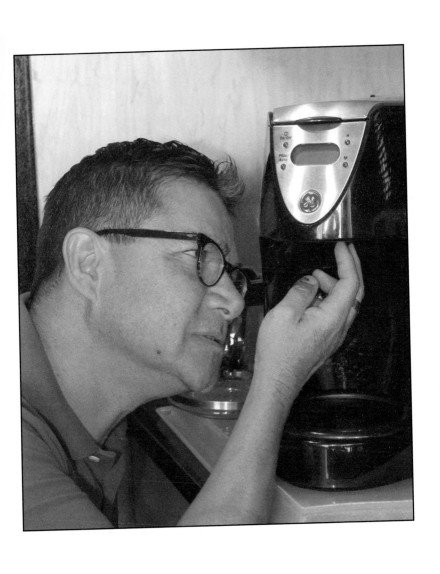

No coffee.

Bo shakes the coffee maker.

He yells, "Come on! Work!"

Dan says, "Dad?"

Bo yells, "What!"

Dan says, "You need to plug it in."